The Moon Wrote a Song

Stories and observations
from the students of 826CHI

The Moon Wrote A Song
© by 826CHI

Cover design: Diana Molleda
Book design: Diana Molleda
Publication Coordinator: Waringa Hunja
Managing Editors: Mackenzie Lynch, Megan Cho, and Emma Kupor

Published by Moody Publications.

Proceeds from your purchase of this publication support 826CHI, a non-profit creative writing, tutoring, and publishing center. www.826chi.org

The views expressed in this book are those of the authors and the authors' imaginations. We support student publishing and are thrilled you picked up this book!

First Edition 826CHI 2017 // Printed in the United States by McNaughton & Gunn.

The illustrations in this book were created by the talented individuals below. We couldn't have made this book without them. To our illustrators: Thank you for inspiring our students to write!

Anna Mielniczuk
Audrey Green
Bobby Reichle
Cheryll Victuelles
Hallye Webb
Ishita Dharap
Jeff Sant
Jeni Crone
Juan Martinez
Kyrstin Rodriguez
Madeline Bennett
Megan Pelto
Patrick Girouard
Tyler Deal
Vani Sobralske

CONTENTS

FOREWARD

Orlando Lara

Writing is hard, and it's not always enjoyable from start to finish. Yes, it is fun to come up with ideas—crazy adventures, kooky, grounded, three-dimensional characters, and unique dialogue. The first part of writing—the idea part—is amazing. Options galore!

Oh! And the end! Shut up about it! That part is even better than the idea part. Not only are you done, but you've created something. And not just anything, but Art. Yes, Art with a capital "A"! Writing is definitely the most accessible and maybe least appreciated of the art forms, but it can very easily become so … boring. Pedestrian was my preferred word there, but I chose a more, well, boring word. Because a lot of the time writing just feels like work. Drats! I'm starting to talk (well, write) about writing. Going to start a new paragraph.

One of the many things I've learned from my years of tutoring at 826CHI is that all of the students have passion. Sure, they may not all have passion for *writing*, but the fire for *something* exists within them. And here's a secret (It's okay, kids don't read forewords anyway.): it's pretty easy to get these students excited about writing by simply asking them questions about what they're thinking. You're welcome.

While working with first-grader Yamilet A. ("Girl Who Brushes Hair"), she was a little hesitant to hit the ground running, to say the least. As she was still mastering her penmanship, we made a bargain: I would physically write for her as long as she created a story based on the photo. Don't make a big stink about it (spoiler alert: this has a happy ending), but even after our deal, she was having trouble focusing. Going back to my journalism training, I implemented the best question you can ever ask anyone: "Why?" I asked Yamilet to simply justify her story, and she did. She started telling me what the girl in her story was doing and why she was doing it. We wrote more in five minutes than we had the previous twenty. *Relax*, we didn't cut into her homework time, which she did remarkably quickly, and more importantly, correctly. Algebra to first graders, huh? What a world. Right! Writing. Yamilet just needed a little encouragement along the way. And let's face it, we can all use that every once in awhile.

Within this chapbook you'll find the passion and creativity that each of these students possess. There was only a small number of illustrations to choose from, and several make multiple appearances in this book, but despite having the same visuals as starting points, everyone saw something different. Whether it's forest critters playing hide-and-seek, having a continental tree-climbing competition, or unseating a monarch, everyone had their own vision.

It may have seemed like work writing these stories, but, by the end, each of these authors came out Artists.

Orlando Lara does comedy. He especially loves improv. Sometimes he's happy. Sometimes he's sad. He always tries his best to make things better and easier for others. Orlando is a volunteer at 826CHI.

IN THIS BOOK . . .

Though each of these stories is as unique as the students who have penned them, you'll notice a few uncanny similarities. Every day at 826CHI, our After-School Tutoring & Writing students write for fifteen minutes in response to a prompt. This semester, students responded to the original illustrations you'll find in this book.

As you soak in the stories and poems, take a close look at the companion illustration that inspired the piece . . . What do you notice? What do you think happened in the moments before? What do you think happened in the moments after? Then pick up a pen and start writing your own story or poem!

CARTOON NETWORK PROMPT: FRIENDSHIP AND EMPATHY

826CHI is working in partnership with the Cartoon Network to help our students expand their sense of empathy, compassion, and exercise their "kindness muscle." Below are empathy-centered prompts that helped our students think hard about friendship and acceptance in their stories. We hope these prompts inspire other students and that they inspire our readers too!

OPTION A: ARE THERE MORE THAN TWO CHARACTERS IN YOUR ILLUSTRATION?

If so, include something in your story about how they became friends! Here are some questions to help you along:

- How did they meet? Describe the setting and situation in vivid detail.

- Did they like each other when they first met? Dislike each other? Feel neutral? Give a few details about their first impressions.

- What was the main event which brought them together as friends? Were there any challenges to becoming friends?

Imagine that you are one of the characters in your illustrations. Who are you? Write from the character's perspective using "I" to narrate the story. What's the best thing about being friends with the other character? What do you admire about them?

OPTION B: DO YOU HAVE ONLY ONE CHARACTER IN YOUR ILLUSTRATION?

If so, imagine that they are someone you know who is having a bad day. Maybe you're best friends with them, maybe you're just acquaintances, or maybe this is the first time you've ever met each other. Why was the character having a bad day? What do you do to help them feel better?

Fishing Moon
ANNA MIELNICZUI

THE MOON WROTE A SONG

Natalie M. | Grade 1

A bee
has a string on his back.
The string
is on the moon.
There is a flute.
The moon is trying
to catch the bee.
The moon wants to
play the flute to the bee.
The moon wrote a song.
The song
was great.

The song is called moonlight.
The moon sings:
Moonlight
Moonlight
is beautiful
because God made the moonlight
Beautiful moonlight
shines in the dark
because God made the moonlight.

MOON LIGHT TO GIVE TO THE NICE EARTH

Karen V. | Grade 3

One day, the Earth was lava and rocks. Venus had water clouds and enjoyable green grass. Earth was jealous, so Earth decided to steal what Venus had.

"Ha ha ha," said Earth, "Look! I have clouds, green grass, and air so people can live." Venus said nothing. "So," Earth said to Venus, "Now who is the lucky one? Me!" Earth bragged and laughed, "Hahahahahahaha!" Earth was so annoying and time went by.

When Moon came to visit Venus, Venus was so sad. Moon tried to cheer him up "Hi Venus. I know you are sad, so I want to give you a surprise," said Moon. "Okay, go ahead," said Venus. "Poof!" said Moon, and there was air, clouds, green grass and people. "Do you love it?" said Moon. "Yes, thanks so much!" said Venus. "You learned your lesson, right?" Moon asked Earth.

Earth said, "Yes I did." Earth learned that you should be happy with what you have.

Juggling Frog
ANNA MIELNICZUK

THE WIDOWING FROG

Ivanova A. | Grade 8

Daylee, a frog, was juggling many emotions. Her house was practically falling apart, piece by piece. She had just lost a husband. This hit her like a tsunami. This frog was confused about how to feel about life—whether to be sad, okay, worried, surprised, or happy. It seemed as if she was going down a path, but she didn't know where to go. Now that he had left, every time she took a step she was further and further away from home. She didn't know her place or position as a frog. She didn't know what to do or how to do it. It seemed as if the only thing that was keeping her together was the very skin that she was in. The path that she was going down had bumps and curves that she couldn't handle. With every bump, the journey got harder, harder to a point that she couldn't take control of it. It was hard to overcome her emotions and grab a handle of her life. This path became so overwhelming to the point where she was losing her form and was ready to give up. She didn't give up. She overcame her emotions by trying to figure out what it was like to live life before she met him. She soon figured out that she had to start from the bottom and work her way up the ladder of success, and she pushed through with her last flower of hope. In the end, she found out that she didn't need to depend on anybody but herself to be happy.

MEMORY LOST

Melissa A. | Grade 6

Once there was a frog named Pepe. Pepe was having a very bad day. Pepe forgot how to juggle and she had been practicing really hard learning how to juggle. Pepe went to her 826 animal school that day and on her way back home she found me walking under the leaf near her house. I was walking near her house because I was on vacation and I got to go on a city tour.

Pepe asked me, "Do you know how to juggle?" I said, "Of course I do. I learned how to juggle in 4th grade." Pepe said, "Can you teach me? Because I forgot how to juggle by eating pollen."

The pollen made her forget how to juggle because it was a pollen that had a lot of sugar and when she eats sugar she loses her memory. The sugar made her lose her memory because she usually eats organic sugar and the pollen had GMO.

I said, "Yeah, sure," so I helped Pepe juggle at the end. Pepe was very happy that her juggling was back!

THE END!

Note: At one point, Pepe became an insect by eating the pollen, she was really big, and then she fell into the lake, after that she ate a fish. The fish made Pepe become a frog again because they used to live in the same place. So the fish gave Pepe some water and the water diluted the sugar so that she wouldn't be an insect anymore. Lastly, she became a frog again the very next day.

Hide-n-Seek Forest Animal

AUDREY GREEN

WARNING: CANADA IS COLD!

Mayra C. | Grade 3

Foxy came and got the best spot to hide.

"I think you will find me first," Lelita said. She hid behind a tree. Foxy said, "Ready or not, here I come," and of course he found her. "Lelita is it," said Foxy.

Lelita started to count even though she knew how to climb trees and she could. She was excited and started to count. She found her friend Beary and she saw Foxy trying to climb a tree.

"That is impressive that you climb a tree as a deer," said Foxy. "I am the queen of trees," said Lelita when she was climbing and staring. Foxy said, "I challenge you to run from Oklahoma to Canada on a tree climbing contest."

Lelita was laughing at Foxy. When the competition started, all the animals saw that Lelita was winning.

The competition plan was first to climb an oak tree, then run to Canada, and climb a syrup tree. Lelita won and everyone was so happy. As they were cheering on Lelita, Foxy was still on the oak tree.

It took Foxy three weeks to run to Canada and two days to climb the two trees. Lelita felt glad and sad because Foxy was not there yet. Foxy was cold in freezing snow. When Lelita got there, Foxy looked like an ice cube.

Lelita had an idea, which was to grab a sled and go down the tree so foxy could get warm. While Lelita pushed the sled, she and Foxy and the sled went all the way back to Oklahoma.

SHADOWLESS
Asha H. | Grade 7

Once there were five friends. One was a fox named Frank, one was a bear named Barry, one was a deer named Rob, one was a bunny named Bob, and the last one was a coyote named Cody. They decided to play a game before the sunrise, so they went to the forest and played hide-and-seek.

When Bob looked back, he saw that Barry was scared the most. A few minutes later, when Bob looked back, he noticed that none of the animals had a shadow. All five animals were scared, so they all ran back home to Bob's. Bob's parents said, "It was just the way the sun was positioned." They went back to the forest, and they ended up back in the same hiding spots. They played all night long.

Barry was "it." Cody, Bob and Frank hid in the bushes with their ears and tails out while Rob hid behind a tree. When the sun rose, they were done playing, and they lived happily ever after.

THE RULER OF THE FOREST
Valeria A. | Grade 3

One night, a squirrel, a deer, a bear and a fox were hanging out, but the fox was very sneaky. The fox was just pretending to be nice to the squirrel, so he could rule the forest!

Then one day, the fox came up with an idea. He asked the squirrel to play hide and seek with him and the others. Everyone went to find a hiding spot. Then, when an animal was counting, the fox was going to go home, but this time there was a fire! The fox saw something in the fire. It was the forest ruler's crown.

The fire vanished, and the fox took the crown to the forest to show the animals. When he got there, everyone was bowing behind him except the squirrel because the crown belonged to her! The fox felt guilty, but he could not move

because he became stone. They never heard from him again.

HIDE AND SEEK

Carolina A. | Grade 8

3, 2, 1, let's begin.

Well, it actually wasn't a beginning. There was no time to hide; you just had to go. The seeker wouldn't say, "Ready or not, here I come." His machine would have said it for him. This time they came in packs of a dozen, or twelve.

"Quick!" yelled Butch the bear, hiding. The beaver, the fox, the cat and the chicken all went running. They didn't say "Begin." Our friend Rigan— she's a duck—was picked up by the ears by these wild men, who walked off. We were already hiding. Silly Rigan, she couldn't play hide and seek.

"Oh no," said Lana the fox, "They got Tina and Toby—" "Cover your ears," said Talina the cat. They covered their ears and eyes and when Butch gave the signal to open their eyes, Tina and Toby were gone and all they saw were their legs being dragged away. Gene the chicken said, "Why are our friends always leaving with these men?"

Tulie, being as smart as she is, answered saying, "I heard they have dinner with the humans, but they never bring them back." "Did they leave us for them?" asked Gene. "I guess so," said Tulie the beaver. "They do know they're supposed to bring them back," said Lana the fox.

Out of nowhere Richy the Wolf came and said, "Oh, you stupid animals. Your friends aren't coming back. You're not safe playing this game with the people. They are not your friends. Your friends are safer with me and my pack than with those wild walking sticks and their packs."

"How do you know?" asked Gene the chicken. "Those people aren't bored men who want to play," said Richy. "Who are they then?" said Tulie. That was uncommon, as Tulie would never be the one to ask questions, but the one to answer them. The animals turned to Tulie and then Richy and then Tulie again.

"They are hunters. . . ," said Richy. What are hunters? They didn't know. Yet Richy knew about hunters all too well. His cousins, brothers, and friends were all taken by hunters. Richy warned the animals of the danger they faced if they kept playing that "game."

"I don't think the game you're thinking of is the same game they're thinking of," said Richy. "W-What does that mean?" said Butch the bear, all panicky-like. "'Game' to them are animals that they hunt to eat for dinner or just for the thrill of being able to ruin something that's bigger than them, and what their society thinks is dangerous or difficult to do," said Richy. "Like a bear?" said Butch the bear. "Like a bear," said Richy. "Like a cat," said Talina. "Sometimes," said Richy. "I see many take out flashing boxes. A man in the back would hold the box while the one in front stands on the animal." "Bye, guys!" said Richy. "I'll see you tomorrow when the moon's out." And he left.

"I don't think they know how to play," said Gene the chicken. "I don't think they know they're playing," said Butch the bear. "Those are mean friends," said Lana the Fox. "They aren't our friends, not anymore anyway," said Tulie the Beaver. "What do they do to the animals again. . . ? They eat them?" "Tina," said Lana the Fox. "Toby," said Butch the bear. "Why would you lie!" said Gene. "What?" said Talina. "You said, you said that they'd have dinner and that the animals would join them. . . as a family!" "She never said anything like that," said Butch. "I figured that's what she meant when she said they were never coming back—" said Lana the Fox. "If you knew they were. . . If you knew they weren't coming back, why would you say they were guests for dinner?" "Ugh, I think I'm gonna throw up,"

"Tina! Toby!" yelled Butch, "Rigan!" he screamed. The bushes in the background started rustling. "Hunters," whispered Lana. The animals all ducked down and started to slowly walk away.

"I overheard one of them saying to another that the animal they had caught was going to make a fine guest for dinner. I thought they meant that they were going to share food with Rigan." "It was Rigan?" sighed

Butch. "I think we need to leave," whispered Gene.

"Yeah," said Tulie. The animals walked away from the area, but before they could, an animal jumped out of the bushes: a rabbit. "Tina!" said Butch.

"Tina?" questioned Lana. "Tina!" screamed Talina.

"Shh, they're right behind me," said Tina. "Who?" said Tulie.

"Hunters," said Tina. "They got me and Toby but I made it out. I need your help. He's in real danger. All the animals were there, every single one of them." "Even Rigan?" Said Butch.

"She didn't come with us. I thought she was still here with you." "No, she went missing a long time ago. I could've sworn I saw one of those men in blue take her." "In blue?" "Yeah, why?" "She's in danger then. The guys that took us were in white, not blue."

They followed Tina out the area and into where the hunters took her and Toby.

DINO IN THE NEW YORK CITY
Terence H. | Grade 2

Once upon a time there was a dino in New York City. He was a T-Rex. He wanted to be in the city because there weren't many storms in the city. He came from a rainforest and didn't like the rain. He was in the city wandering around, looking at the buildings to find a place to sit down and take a nap.

The police heard him stomping in the dark. The police woke up and they grabbed their flashlights and tried really, really hard to find the dino. They looked on top of, behind, and in front of buildings. They searched for a long, long time. It was very cold outside. Everybody woke up in the middle of the night. They went to their porches and saw the dino walking around outside the Ace hotel. Everybody came to Chicago because the dino was starting to knock down towers in New York City. The police built a 20,000,000 feet tall robot that could put big handcuffs on the dino and had a big laser hand. When they finished, the police were 20,000,000 years old. Now, back to the laser part. The laser could cut off a part of the island with the dino on it. When the dino got to the other island, he walked right into a 200-foot jail. Now everyone could come back to New York City. They were saved!

Dinosaur In The City
BOBBY REICHLE

NO TACOS FOR YOU TODAY

Brandon A. | Grade 5

Once, there was a girl named Kelly. She was on her phone talking to Brandon about the monster who likes tacos. Brandon was a boy she liked in school and he liked her back. They got off the phone in the night, and then Kelly heard really hard stomping, which she thought to be an earthquake. When she looked back, she saw the monster. She wanted to take a picture to show Brandon.

But she opened the photos app too late, and she only got a picture of the tail of the monster. Brandon did not believe Kelly because Brandon thought the tail in the picture was a taco. So Brandon put a song about tacos in his text to Kelly. Kelly texted, "No tacos for you today!" to Brandon.

After texting Brandon, Kelly ran to take another picture. When she got there, the monster faced her and its face looked like the Grinch. Kelly took the picture and ran away. The monster ran to get Kelly, because the monster thought that Kelly was a taco. Kelly ran to the nearest taco shop.

Then, she went inside the taco shop and sent the photo to Brandon to prove that the monster was real. When Brandon looked at it, he freaked out and ran outside to look for Kelly. Then, Kelly bought tacos for the monster and herself. She came out of the taco shop and gave the tacos to the monster. The monster grabbed a taco and ate it, and the monster said "Mmmmmm."

Brandon walked by and saw Kelly eating tacos with the monster. Brandon said, "What the heck, what the heck? What the heck is that!"

Then, Kelly said, "No tacos for you today!"

THE ONLY DINOSAUR ON EARTH

Jeury M. | Grade 5

A dino was separated from his family in Chicago during the fire and was taken to New York City by rescue workers.

One day, in New York City, a man found the dino. The man said, "It's green, it's huge!" He called the cops, but the dino just walked into an alley and hid behind a tree! The cops found him easily because he was giant. He couldn't fit into a cop car, not even his toes, so they used godzilla tranquilizers, and he roared in pain and fell. Even Mexico heard it. His teeth were as big as an adult's head.

They chained him, but he broke the chains. He ran to the Empire State Building and hung on it like King Kong. All the people fainted. Then he jumped and smashed a school bus and used it like a skateboard. He did an ollie. When he landed it felt like an earthquake.

He went to the Statue of Liberty and took the torch. Then, he threw it away because it reminded him of when there was a big fire in Chicago, and when he got separated from his parents and went to New York with his toy human.

Finally, he left New York and was never found again.

BUNNY FAMILY WAS THE HAPPIEST FAMILY EVER

Jane S. | Grade 4

Eva was a mommy bunny with her two babies. One was Emma and the other one was Bluey. They lived in a castle. One day, they were in the garden. The mommy was reading a book and Emma was at the slide when Bluey got hurt at the monkey bars. Bluey got hurt because his hands slipped. Bluey watched a movie inside because he got hurt.

Emma was at the slide and she got hurt too, so she went to her mom. She was hurt in her head, as well as at the front and the back of her legs. She watched the movie *Elsa* with her brother because she got hurt. Then they got better. Then they lived happily ever after, so they had fun again.

Bunny Castle
VANI SOBRALSKE

GIANT FURRY

Isaias D. | Grade 6

Once upon a time, I heard something in the woods. It was really loud. It sounded like the stomping of a big dinosaur's foot. It was so loud my parents woke up. We lived near the woods, that's why it was so loud. My parents fell back asleep, but I got out of my bed and went outside. When I opened the door I saw something big but I couldn't see it well. So then I ran to the kitchen to get a flashlight and a broom. Then I ran back and it was still there.

When I turned on the flashlight, it was a giant, furry, giraffe-looking creature. It wasn't scared of me, so I got close to it and petted it, and I gave it a name. It was Furry. I noticed he liked that name because he started jumping around. He let me on his back and we climbed a mountain. When we reached the top of the mountain we were above the clouds. It was so cool and I was so amazed, but I was tired. Then a few moments later I fell asleep and when I woke up, I was in my bed. I looked out the window and it was open.

I saw a piece of fur that Furry left. That's when I figured out it wasn't a dream, it was real life.

The Creature and The Boy
JEFF SANT

THE WELL-RESTED MAX AND BOBBY

Crystal M. | Grade 7

Once upon a time, there was a weird creature and his buddy Max. The creature's name was Bobby. Bobby and Max were best friends with the BFG and Sophia. Bobby and Max always wanted to visit Cloudy Mountain. Cloudy Mountain was located in two places: Paris and London.

The reason why Bobby and Max went to the Cloudy Mountain in London was because Bobby and Max went to the one in Paris and they wanted to try out the one in London. They got up the mountain because Bobby had long legs that could expand. Bobby could also fly. When he flew, he took Max to Big Ben because Max had always wanted to visit Big Ben. After visiting Big Ben, they went to Cloudy Mountain to relax because it was peaceful. Bobby and Max wanted to rest after the long day. Cloudy Mountain had a nice view, and it helped Max go to sleep. Cloudy Mountain smelled like cupcakes and rainbows. The sounds they heard were birds chirping. They loved the sounds of the birds chirping everyday!

When they got to the top, they both looked at the view. People could see Bobby because Bobby had a power, which was to expand his legs and fly. Max was small compared to Bobby. When they were looking down from from the top of the mountain, they saw the whole city of London! They also saw shooting stars. The shooting stars helped Max sleep. When he woke up, Bobby took Max to school well-rested.

ROAMING THE UNIVERSE

Julian V. | Grade 6

I was a mole named Banana. I was going to Mars. "It is on Earth," I said.

The farm chicken said, "It is in space."

It was on Earth—according to Google Moles on my phone—Mars was 1,000,000 miles away. *Wow, okay,* I thought. I set the sails to the sea to get to Mars. *No!* My phone fell in the water.

Later on, a big wave came. I got somewhere. Then I told the chicken to find my phone. He said, "No!" I used a fan to go faster but did not succeed. The chicken went to sleep.

At first, all I could see was water, not land nor Mars. Then I found land. *What!* It was the chicken land. "No!" I said, "Where is Mars?" The chickens on the chicken land laughed.

I built a rocketship. Suddenly, my boat was carrying the rocketship. All of a sudden, the rocketship popped! I fell with the boat to the water. Then I was lost.

I found land again and said, "I found Mars!" Now I was the first of 10,000,000 people to set foot on Los Angeles. I screamed, "I found Mars!"

The farm chicken said, "It is not Mars. It's Los Angeles."

Then my boat and I went off to find Pluto.

AN ANTEATER AND GIANT SQUAD

Carlos P. | Grade 5

One day, there was an anteater king. He lost his crown by dropping it down in the ocean, deep, deep down, somewhere hidden. He knew where it had landed. It was by a giant squid with eyes the size of an elephant. He wanted to get it back but he didn't know where the giant squid lived. The anteater thought, *I think it is far away, but how am I going to get it?* His mind was trying to trick him. *It's in a volcano. No, no,* the anteater king said to his brain. So he hid waterproof cameras around the deep ocean and he stared up to twenty-four hours at the screen to look. Two days later, he saw the giant squid. The anteater king looked at him and saw where he lived.

The giant squid's home was like a dream home. The only thing the anteater king knew was that the giant squid was a snob and always yearned to tell people to be his guard. The anteater king hacked into the giant squid's computer and saw he had the crown in his profile. He had the crown that looked like it was made of diamonds, gold, rubies, silver, and iron. The crown was the size of a penny. The giant squid had his crown. He had large armies and always wore only socks that he made out of garbage.

The anteater king went out to look from house to house to find the giant squid's house to get his crown back. When the giant squid dropped the crown, it landed on the anteater king's head and he said, "Problem solved."

The End

The Mole Castle in The Bo

JEFF SANT

THE CROWNED-HEAD MOLE LIVING WITH STUFF LIKE BEARKATS GOES ON AN ADVENTURE

Logan H. | Grade 6

Once, there was a king mole in a big castle. Other weird animals lived in the citadel, such as a bearkat, which was literally a cat that looked like a bear and smelled like buttery popcorn. They needed gold and rations because their castle was in a remote area. The crowned-head king mole was trying to find out where to get what they needed, then he remembered they had a boat nearby in the ocean. They went to fix the ship. It was old and the propeller didn't work underwater so they put it on the top of the back of the boat.

When it was time to leave, the king decided he wanted to take the castle, but it was much too large, so he cut off the top. The crowned-head wanted all of the animals to come so he told them to get in the piece of the castle he cut off, and he put it on the boat. The mole was really big so he had to stay on top of the castle, on top of the boat, and watch their path as they went. After one month of sailing, they got to a wonderland full of gold and food.

Gold was gold but food came in many different varieties. Each food was from a different country, region, or cuisine. It was amazing, but as they went on they recognized each feast came with a cost to get there. Once they even had to defeat an army in planes! Another time they had to climb a giant Jenga tower to Mars without making the tower fall, but the adventures to get the food were usually fun.

SHE LEFT HER HOMEWORK IN INDIA

Miles D. | Grade 3

Jennifer was a nineteen-year-old actress in college. One day, Jennifer was looking for her homework. She was so obsessed with her homework that she forgot to feed her cat for five days in a row. The cat got so hungry that he chewed up her homework.

She had an idea. Jennifer and her friend had the same homework. When she left, her cat hid in her bedroom. When she got back, nothing had happened to the cat. Jennifer got a copy from her friend and quickly did the five pages that were due and turned it in online.

The next week, she went to India because there was a movie premiere happening. And she left her homework in India! She was definitely going to get an F because her homework was due in ten minutes and it was in India.

She looked for her cat Max, but she couldn't find him anywhere. She screamed. She screamed really loudly. She passed the heart-shaped flowers which were her cat Max's. An hour later, she finally found Max the cat. She had a sixty-story-tall bed, in which she put Max so he wouldn't jump down, but she forgot he was a cat. Max jumped off the sixty-story bed. Max was in the plants again and stayed in the plants.

CREEPERS

Fernando A. | Grade 7

Crawlers are these tiny black creatures with legs that can be mistaken for leaves. These creatures are very stealthy. Crawlers are most common in any open space in your home. Crawlers sometimes hide among other plants. Be careful when touching plants, one sting from them can lead you to start seeing hallucinations. The body of these creatures can only grow up to the size of a quarter, but their legs can be at least twelve inches long, which is the size of a tiny dog.

There is a story where there was a crawler in a man's mug. The crawler was unharmed when he came in contact with the boiling hot coffee. The man threw his coffee and he burned himself. He later came to work late, so his boss fired him.

A jogger spotted a crawler at a park. It distracted him for a while, because the crawler made a quick movement causing him to stumble back and run into somebody on a bike. This was all recorded and uploaded to social media. He was embarrassed.

Three little boys spotted one of these at their school park. They poked it with a twig and it jumped onto them, then to a tree. After, there were groups of kids who played different sports. When one of the boys was playing tag, he got hit in the face with a basketball, then a soccer ball, then a football, and finally a volleyball.

Some say this creature causes more bad luck than a black cat. One day, about sixty crawlers found their way into a grocery store. They ate most of the fruits and creeped everyone out. The store went out of business since nobody went back. Be careful, there can be a crawler next to you right now.

Hiding in Plants
MEGAN PELTO

MY BEST FRIEND

Ariana B. | Grade 6

I looked at myself in my mirror, but there was a different person inside. She had a black coat, a white mask, and the same balloon as I had. She was the opposite of me and looked like my friend. She had a balloon that looked the same as mine. My balloon had a smiley face just like hers. I liked balloons because they are like pets. My balloon's name was Billy Jo Bob. I met the balloon at the carnival when I won him in the slam dunk. It was fun. Sometimes I felt like he would fly away one day to be in a better place.

I had always wanted a best friend, but I didn't think I had one. She looked like my friend because she looked like the opposite of me, as if we were meant to be friends. A best friend is someone who is there for you and is like a sister, but a way better sister. Her name is Yaretzy. We became friends when I was in 4th grade. I don't know how, but it just happened. She is like a sister for me. She is always so nice to me and always helps me. She is shorter than me and has long hair, and she always wears cat ears. I think I have a best friend after all.

Balloon Girl
KYRSTIN RODRIGUEZ

THE MASKED GIRL

Mariana M. | Grade 7

Who knows this girl? In a black mask, her reflection was the opposite color, had no hands, and had a balloon connected to her extra-large shirt. The Masked Girl was what they called her. She was a bit odd. She stared at her reflection often, for a very long time.

Then she walked into a clothing shop. *Well, Japan is a big place. There are a lot of clothing shops!* she thought. She bought new shoes and went home. Before she went to try on her Vans, she went to the mirror, wondering why her reflection was the opposite, then decided to touch her reflection and actually felt someone else's hand! The masked girl was shocked and in panic. "Who are you?" she screamed. "I am you, in the mirror, a reflection," it screamed back.

The masked girl ran outside and decided to take off her mask. She had never seen her face. *Who am I, really?* she asked herself, then started sobbing. She was on the sidewalk crying for five minutes. *Maybe this was meant to happen,* she thought. *I need to go find myself.* For some reason she decided to go to Paris to find herself. She planned a flight on Monday. Her name? Her name was actually Masked Girl, but after that day she changed her name to Mei Xnang, because she liked the way it sounded.

Mei Xnang was ready to leave Japan for Paris, a place where everyone did not know her. It was a new beginning. Mei started to go to a store to buy new clothes. She bought seven new pairs of shirts and pants, twelve pairs of shoes, and five dresses. After, she went to a jewelry store to buy chokers, necklaces, a lot of bracelets, two purses, and four backpacks. Mei threw away all her old clothes because it reminded her of her reflection.

Mei was a billionaire because of family and used to never buy new clothes or eat at a restaurant. She had long black hair, was five feet, ten inches tall, nineteen years old, and had arms but used to cover them with her long sleeves.

Mei was not going to cook that night. Mei decided to go to a restaurant and treat herself. She threw out all her furniture, sold her mansion, then went to book a hotel room for a night and brought all two of her suitcases into her hotel. "I'm so excited, I'm going to Paris tomorrow!"

Mei was on her way to her private jet and took both of her suitcases. She took a photo with her brand new phone, the Samsung 8. The photo was captioned: "Goodbye, Japan! And Hello, Paris!" Twelve hours later, it changed to: "Hello, Paris!" Mei was so excited.

She was in Paris, the place known for love. Mei was a bit confused with how it felt to be loved. She decided to go to the movies and see a romantic movie. She cried a bit but still didn't understand. She went back to the hotel she was staying in and went to sleep. In three months she would start online college.

The next morning, she ate eggs and diced up hot dogs for breakfast and some beans on the side. Today Mei wanted to try a new dessert she never tried in her life, so she went to a big Parisian bakery and tried the strawberry macaroons. Mei bit into the macaroons and a whole big explosion of strawberry and banana hit her mouth.

She left the bakery and went to Starbucks and ordered a pumpkin spice latte. She decided to take her brand new laptop out of her new backpack she bought in Paris. She decided she didn't want to stay in a hotel anymore, so she went fancy, five-star apartment-shopping on her new laptop.

She found a big apartment for her that had two bedrooms, three bathrooms, three floors, two offices, one kitchen, and three living rooms. She decided to click on it and take it. She would move in on Wednesday. She was excited. That night, she celebrated.

The next day she decided to take a tour around Paris. She was thinking about landmarks. She thought of the Eiffel Tower.

She decided to buy an aqua scooter. She had her Paris license and drove to the Eiffel Tower. She found parking and decided to buy top floor tickets. Mei wanted to eat breakfast. She was starving. She got all the way to the top. When she went in the elevator, which went to the restaurant, the first thing she got there was a chicken alfredo fettuccine.

She finished eating. She had her phone and camera out. She was ready to take photos. She looked at the view. She wasn't aware of how high she was! She could see the whole city. One hour later, she was ready to leave.

Mei's camera fell on the ground. This random boy came and picked it up for her. This tender feeling hit her chest and she started to blush, a feeling she she had never had. *What is this feeling?* She asked herself.

"Hey, I'm Adam White. You new here?"

"Yeah, I'm Mei Xnang!"

Three years later...

Mei and Adam had been dating for two years already. She now understood what love is and she was really successful in college. She had studied three languages: French, English, and Italian.

To be continued...

CURLY TANGO

Cynthia O. | Grade 8

Tangled hair everywhere
My hair
Full of curls
A nice dim brown
Fly, fly, is what they say to each other
Dancing Tango all over me
I'm struggling to brush my hair
But I sure like it
Morning and night, 24/7
You will see
A girl brushing her hair
After every meal, even snack
My hair
Is everywhere
So what, don't judge
I may look ugly but I am surely a happy girl!
Now on my way to downtown
To meet up with the people that say nonsense
I don't know how to deal with that
I'm a mess, how am I going to do this!
I can do it
I'm going to go there,
And my words will shine
Like my dancing curls
Everything is possible . . .
Everything is possible!
My hair may be a mess
But . . .
At the end of the day,
It's all silky and beautifully untangled!

Girl Brushing Hair
ISHITA DHARAP

GIRL WHO BRUSHES HAIR
Yamilet A. | Grade 1

The girl is throwing out plates, throwing out spoons, closing her eyes and covering her ears because the sound of the plates and spoons is so loud that even the neighbors can hear it. Her name is Zelda. It's night and she is asleep. She is throwing plates because she doesn't know her story, but she can't wake up because it's night.

Zelda must sleep. If she doesn't, she'll be sleepy in the morning, and then she'll be sleepy in school. But she wants good grades, like A's. Zelda wants to be a learner.

THE PLANETS SHE ADORED
Valery V. | Grade 2

One night, a girl was brushing her curly black hair that was three meters long. She had two plates, mugs, a bowl, a spoon and a fork. Her name was Abigail. She was imagining playing music with the stars and the plates, mugs, bowl, spoon and fork. She was pretending to be in the galaxy in her room, because there was a window that showed her the galaxy. It looked black, purple, and blue.

She felt like she was in outer space. Then she became a part of the galaxy, because she had a magic brain. She played with all the planets. Her favorites were Pluto and Earth. Then she went back to her room and played with the plates and the planets she adored. Then she got really sleepy and dreamed of taking her family to the galaxy.

BIT OF THE MOON

Angel G. | Grade 8

There was once a girl who loved to find out the sounds of forks, spoons, and plates. She would gently hit the spoon and forks against the table to find out what sound they make. She came up with an idea and thought, *what sounds do the spoon and fork make together?* The sound the spoon and fork made was a high-pitch bang. Then she tried plates, teacups, and a gravy bowl as she fell asleep.

She then dreamt about being in her bed and closing her eyes, and then the house teleported to the desert. Her window was opened by a huge breeze while she was making music with the kitchenware. The breeze blew her hair and as the breeze came to some of the plates and spoons, they started to make sounds. She spent the whole time in her dreams thinking about how wonderful it was to be there. But in reality, she was sitting down on her bed and thinking about how her life was going.

Then she opened her eyes and walked to the window and with her warm last breath she looked up to the stars and then . . . she saw the most beautiful bit of the moon.

BEEGIRL

Kristupas R. | Grade 5

The
 girl who
 flies
 with
 the bees
 she rides
 in her
    bee ship
   she flies
  with them
   and populates
   in the beehive
  she goes
 flower
  to flower
  and eats
   honey every
  day to
     compare flowers
    to the
    end
     the bad thing about honey
    is that humans
     eat
     too much.

Bee Girl
PATRICK GIROUARD

BEE GIRL

Yareli A. | Grade 1

"I will not be scared," the girl said. "I will go to the bee's house. The bees are my friends."

The girl said that she and her friends would stay at the bee's house. They would go and buy honey and a lot of bread. The bees and the girl would also eat Nutella with their bread. After they eat, they were going to go to the park. They were going to get some blood.

She would sleep there. The bees and the girl would get sunflowers at the flower stand. The flower stand was far away. It would take twenty minutes to get there. They would need hats and heavy clothes because it was 20° Fahrenheit. They would need pillows and yellow and black pajamas.

THE ROBOT

Keontae M. | Grade 6

One day, there was a kid named John. He didn't have friends. He was in a world where there were robots to solve human problems. Even the robots wouldn't ask him what was wrong.

Later that day, John was walking to the store. There was hotel construction happening, but John wasn't looking where he was going. He was on his phone.

The construction workers were screaming, "Watch out, kid!" He kept walking. He was close to falling, but, out of nowhere, a robot came and swept John up into his hands.

"Why did you save me?" John said.

"All robots have to solve human problems," said the robot.

"But I don't understand. I want to get hurt. Nobody likes or pays attention to me," said John.

"But I have to pay attention to you because us robots solve all human problems," said the robot.

"Why do you solve all human problems?" said John.

"We were made in a factory by a man named Josh. He took control of us because he was having a hard time. He was always tripping, falling, and being irresponsible, so he made robots and put them to work. He made us go shopping and do paperwork. He made us do dishes, start the car, clean the table for dinner, get the table ready for dinner, and put him to sleep. But, when we put him to sleep, we escaped out the front door. Instead of solving Josh's problems we decided to solve all human problems. That's why I saved you from falling," said the robot.

"Wow, I wish I could solve human problems so people would pay attention to me," said John.

"Pay attention to where you are going," said the robot.

"But I want to die because I have no friends," said John.

Helicopter Boy
PATRICK GIROUARD

"Well, now you do have a friend," said the robot.

When the robot looked down, he saw Josh. Josh was standing outside looking for the robots that solved his problems. "Robots, where are you, robots?" said Josh.

"Oh, no," said the robot.

"What, what, what is it?" said John.

"It's Josh, and he's looking for us," said the robot.

"We have to go now. Josh is looking for us to do his work for him," said the robot. Josh saw the robot in the air.

"Hey, come back here now!" said Josh.

"No, I'm not doing your dirty work," said the robot. The robot flew off with the kid and they were never found again.

THE HELICOPTER AND THE BOY

Antonio A. | Grade 3

Once there was a helicopter and a boy. The helicopter was very shiny. The boy's name was Antonio. He was 4-foot-3 and had dark hair. Also, the boy wore jeans and a white shirt. The helicopter fell from the sky, and the boy almost got hit. The little boy had a box of tools, and he went over to see what was wrong with the helicopter. The boy fixed the helicopter with his tools. The helicopter asked the boy if he would like to be friends. The boy said yes. The helicopter took the boy home, and they tested the helicopter. There was a screw that was missing so the wing fell off. He fixed the wing so it looked brand new.

Antonio said, "I need some help, too. I'm bad at reading."

"I can help you with that! I can take you to this place called 826CHI," said the helicopter.

When he was done with 826CHI, he met this guy named Jeury. Jeury had a red shirt and black sweatpants on. Jeury got into the helicopter and fell out, but he had a parachute. Jeury walked home. Antonio went home too. The helicopter took Antonio home.

SQUALIEN

Courtney M. | Grade 5

In this picture, I see five scuba divers swimming around this huge squid. This squid has huge black eyes and many suckers—if I were to make an estimate, I would say 20,000 suckers. I think the scuba divers are amazed and curious about how big it is, don't you think?

If I saw a squid like that, I would have swam up to the top like a race car. Wait, that's not all I have to say about this drawing. This squid has a very, very, very big head, maybe it has a very big brain inside that big head. I think this squid is the biggest squid ever. I think this squid is as tall as the White House. I think this squid is from the aliens' planet and came here to make friends. Maybe the squid's name is . . . *Squalien!* From *Squanit* planet. Maybe *Squalien* is coming to take us to a field trip to *Squanit* planet. Until then . . . To be continued . . .

Scuba Divers And Giant Squid
TYLER DEAL

THE WONDERS DOWN BELOW
Diego R. | Grade 6

One hot, mucky day, there were four scuba divers: Diego, Jen, Bob, and Zoe. It was time for them to go on a deep sea adventure. All four were sitting on a boat and then they dove into the water. The sea had fish and amazing coral reefs. They were swimming deep down in the water when a long, dark figure darted past them. They all began to worry when, right then, something rushed by their backs. Something dark flew by them!

They looked around and saw bubbles that were made by something large and fast. They swam as fast as they could to the top of water when something grabbed Jen and Bob. Diego and Zoe couldn't leave their friends behind, so, trembling with fear, they rushed after the creature. It was too fast to catch so they followed the bubbles it had left behind. The bubbles were in a weird, zig-zag lines that led to a broken down submarine.

They started searching when something broke through a wall and into the next room. They rushed in and saw bodies covered in slime. The people looked alive but also very hot which meant in any minute they would go crazy because of how hot it was. They were searching around more when a giant squid took Zoe to a throne covered in jewels and rare shark teeth. The squid had one eye. Diego saw the other eye was gone! The squid was also purple with little spikes coming out of its head.

"Zoe!" screamed Diego. Diego was terrified because Zoe had been his crush for a long time. Suddenly, the throne turned around revealing . . . JACK! Jack was his enemy because they had both fought for Zoe but now Jack had a perfect plan. He captured Zoe and was going to win. Diego was raging with anger. He grabbed his laser and shot at a button that let the people covered in slime out. All the people fell out, including Jen and Bob who came to help. They took down the squid and Jen laser-cuffed Jack. They helped the people under the water and took Jack to jail.

They finally could go home. All of them were tired and hungry. Diego would go home and play games and eat pizza. Jen would go home and watch TV. Bob would go home and play soccer. Zoe would go home and play with her dog.

THE STORY OF BETTY

Natalia A. | Grade 5

Once upon a time, there was a girl. This girl's name was Betty. Betty was pretty stubborn. Betty would say: "I, myself, only believe in facts." She said she did not have this so-called "imagination."

When Betty was younger, her grandfather told her the story of the floating town. Betty did not believe this story. She said it was impossible.

Her grandfather asked her, "Do you have an imagination?"

She replied, stubbornly, "No. I do not, and I never will."

Long after this conversation, her grandfather passed away. She started to think, *could this story be true?* Betty started to search for the floating town that her grandfather told her about in the story. She tried to use facts and research to get her to the town, but it did not get her anywhere. She tried to imagine herself there and, to her surprise, she found her way there. She got to the town and started an amazing community. The population was 501, but it was quite the vacation spot. In the town you could ride ostriches, which is strange because ostriches are flightless.

Once Betty found the floating town, she tried to make it very welcoming and magical. She made many farms for ostriches. The ostriches always had a safe place to live. Since the town was floating, Betty would send down invitations in clouds. The clouds would act like envelopes. In the letters it would say: *Look up at the town in the sky. If you would like to move here, an ostrich will come down and pick you up.* The whole town knew the story of Betty, since she was the founder. Betty and the townspeople wanted to create their own holidays. They would celebrate the usual holidays, but they would include their own in the calendars. Every night she could hear her grandfather telling her, "I knew you would find your way."

A SMALL CAKE TOWN
Sebastian V. | Grade 2

I saw in the microscope, a small town of cake. There was a flag, and cake people lived there. On the second layer, there were candy bones. There were lots of little houses. The town was made out of cake. There was a place full of water!

There was someone named Sam. Sam liked to read and write. He wrote about how his days were. He got good grades and made comic books. His comic books were about fighting villains. He wrote about villains because they were bad guys. Sam was the guy who made the cake town. The cake town smelled like lots of sweets. That was why Sam ate the cake.

Sam ate pieces of cake. The cake people had to get in the shelter but it was too late for them to shelter. Sam ate all the cakes, swallowing the whole cake at once. The cake people ended up living in Sam's stomach. Then they started to build lots of houses.

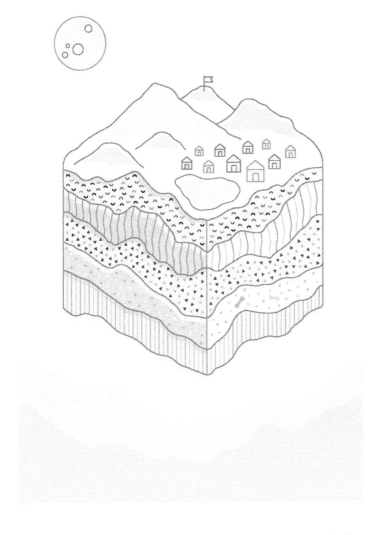

A Small Mountain Town
MADELINE BENNETT

THE CAKE WORLD

Cristian C. | Grade 3

Once upon a time, there were ten houses and five mountains. The mountains had one flag, and the flag was in blue, red, and yellow. The people in the houses lived in a district called the Cake World. The Cake World was always cloudy. There was an ocean in front of the houses. There were people in the houses who had lived in the Cake World for a long time and chose to live there. They arrived to the Cake World by a boat. The mountains were made of sprinkles.

The people liked living in the Cake World. Then, there was a flood coming towards the Cake World. They got a warning on TV. The flood crashed the houses and the people hurried to climb on the five mountains to be safe. The volcano under the water caused the water to flood Cake World. When the volcano stopped moving the water, the water went down and it became sunny. After it became sunny, the people built the houses on the mountain so their houses couldn't be destroyed by the flood again.

IF THE TREE COULD TALK

Morgan A. | Grade 3

One day, there was a robot named Robot. And yes, that was his real name. He was laying on a tree, when suddenly the tree said, "Get off of me!" Robot jumped high up in the air and the tree said, "Why did you lie on me, kid!" "I'm sorry Mr. Olive!" said Robot. "Hey, I'm not Olive," said the tree. "Well, what is your name if your name is not Olive?" said Robot. "My name is Mr. Book," said the tree. "Wow!" said Robot, "What a beautiful name! My name is Robot." "Cool, dude!" said Mr. Book. Then, a bird landed on Robot's head and said, "Now I'm your pet!" Robot was thinking, *what?* Then, they went to sleep for eighty hours, and the next day they had strong muscles. They were all twenty years old, and the bird got lost and never found Robot again.

Robot and Mr. Book had a party because they got 8,000 dollars for winning the lottery. They had a nice friendship because they had parties and ate tacos. They always had fun until a guy came along.

His name was Cargo. Cargo always told lies, which broke Robot and Mr. Book's friendship. For example, he said to Robot that Mr. Book was having a party with a different guy named Plate. Then Cargo said to Mr. Book that Robot had gone to get tacos with a girl robot.

LOL. Anyways, I am the writer of this book and will give Mr. Book and Robot ten books and ice creams every day. They will have to save some ice cream. If they don't both eat ice cream every day, they will need a big fridge. Cargo and Robot and Mr. Book met up. All they wanted to know was why they had parties with someone else or had tacos with someone else, but they argued for at least two hours.

Robot and Mr. Book said, "Wait, how do you know that we had a party or had tacos with someone else?" Cargo wasn't that smart, so he panicked. Mr. Book and Robot saw his sweat before he ran away. Robot had an idea right away and tied Cargo up and took off his lazer bracelet.

The Hill With Eyes
JUAN MARTINEZ

THE HILL

Leah B. | Grade 7

Once there was a man who would always read the same book under the same exact hill of wood chips. One day, he tried to go up the hill, but it just kept drifting away. After that, he just went home. At home, he went to his bedroom. Then he lay down and started to read his book. The day after that, he went back to the park and the hill was gone. He went to find the perfect tree. There wasn't the perfect tree to be leaned on, so he looked back at where the hill was supposed to be. It was there, so he ran over to it. When he ran to the hill, he saw that the hill had eyes. He ran straight to his house, and the large pile of wood chips chased him all the way home. The next day, he didn't go to the park.

He had a dream about the hill. His dream was that he went to go sit on the hill, sank into the hill, and never made it back out. He freaked out. After a whole week of not going to the park, he just got over the whole hill thing. He went to the park and there were four hills of wood chips and they all started drifting towards him. After that, he never went to the park again.

PIGS AND TURTLES

Jaritza M. | Grade 7

Once upon a time, there were two pigs named Winnie and Olive. They wanted to go someplace different from home. They wanted to move to the lake so they could have fun and do something new that they could tell their pig friends about. They called their turtle friends named Shelly and Speedy and they took them to the lake.

The pigs were happy to go to the lake, but Winnie and Olive's friends doubted them. The pigs went to prove the opposite. Olive wanted to live in the water, so he could prove that pigs could swim.

Olive said, "The water is cold," and then he drowned. The turtle saved Olive. They went home and lived safely.

"Thanks," said Olive.

Pigs And Turtles
CHERYLL VICTUELLES

THE BLUE RIVER LAKE

Alondra A. | Grade 2

There are two ugly pigs and two wet turtles. One turtle is named Steven and the other one is Missy. The pigs jumped on the turtles' backs. One pig is Lilly, and the other pig is a wolf wearing a pig costume. They're on a dirty lake, and the Turtles are floating heavily. They like to feel the air. Lilly is sitting on Steve and the other is laying on the back of Missy. The pigs are acquaintances. No one is having fun. Because they are bored. Because it is so hot.

They would all rather play hide-and-seek tag. When you find the person, you have to tag them. The pigs are tired. So they want to go to sleep instead.

The turtles say, "That's okay. We are too busy to play anyway." The turtles go home, and the pigs stay and become friends.

SAM AND MAX

Sipho F. | Grade 4

Once there were pigs from the pig planet where the pigs lived. The names of the pigs were Max, who was blue and red, and Sam, who was orange and violet. Max and Sam were on a trampoline. They jumped so high that gravity took them to a different planet.

Once they landed, there were surfing turtles. The turtles surfed all down the river and took Max and Sam to a cave where they were going to live for their lives. They ate fish in their cave and their bed was stone.

Max said, "I wonder why this new planet smells like eggs and looks like slime?" When they looked up, there was a big egg and slime coming down from the sky, so to keep the smell out of the cave they closed the entrance with wood and created a door. That way Sam and Max could live there with no egg smell.

THE MYSTERY OF THE GIANT GOLDFISH

Isaiah O. | Grade 8

Once upon a time, in the magical land of Las Vegas, there was a fish. A ginormous goldfish. This goldfish was over six feet tall and was about fifty pounds altogether. Nobody was quite sure why the fish was there or where it came from, and no one wondered either. The fish was known for . . . blowing bubbles, just like any other fish, which was exactly why nobody went to see it anymore.

One day, a young girl named Raya saw the fish on the news while her father, Peter, was in his room working on some reports. "Daddy! Daddy! Daddy!" She yelled. "Yes, honey," Peter said from his room. "Everybody has stopped seeing the giant fish!" It was silent for a second.

"Daddy! Come here!"said Raya. A sigh came from the other room. "Honey," he said as he walked into the room where Raya was, "I'm really busy, and I still have a ton of reports to finish. And—" He stopped and looked down at Raya, who was making her famous puppy-dog eyes. He smiled and said, "Oh, you know I can't resist those adorable eyes of yours . . . " Raya smiled and started talking.

"Daddy," she said. "Nobody cares about the giant fish anymore!" Peter looked at her. "And why is that?" he asked. "Well," Raya said, "The news lady says the fish is boring because it just swims in circles and blows bubbles just like any other fish in the sea." Raya looked up at her father, "I want to see that fish!" "But honey," he started, "You still have school, and I don't know if I could take off wor—" "But daddy, please!" Raya interrupted, "Nobody wants to see the fishy, and it probably feels lonely!"

Peter was about to say something when he looked into Raya's eyes. He could see a fierce determination to go see the fish. This little girl wanted to see this fish, and she wasn't going to take no for an answer. "I-I'll see what I can do . . . " Peter didn't want to let his daughter down, but what if he couldn't take off work? What if his boss threatened to fire him? He couldn't lose this job! This was his fourth job in the last six months! But he couldn't let her down. He was willing to do whatever it took to take this little girl to see that goldfish.

That night, Peter was on the American Airlines website looking for tickets to Las Vegas. The more Peter looked at the airplane tickets, the more he thought about reconsidering the trip. I mean, those tickets were expensive! Peter got up to tell Raya that they might need to postpone the trip, but, when he walked into her room, he saw her sleeping so peacefully. She really wanted this, and he had to give it to her. He couldn't let her down no matter what. So, that night, he bought the tickets.

ONE WEEK LATER . . .

It was a Saturday. Peter had gotten up at 6:30 in the morning to tell his boss about the trip. "But please!" he shouted, "She needs to see that fish!" Peter's boss looked at him. It was a mean old lady with a face that was permanently stuck in a frown.

"If you go, there's no guarantee that you'll be able to keep your job," she said. "But, why can't you understand?!" Peter shouted, "I just want to let my little girl have a better life than I had!"

His boss was sitting on her desk and staring at the floor. "You know I have a daughter of my own," she said. "And when she was little, all I ever wanted was to give her the world. Just because I'm your boss doesn't mean I don't understand where you're coming from." Her eyes were getting watery. A good five minutes passed before she spoke again. "I'll do what I can," she said, "I will try my best to keep your job yours, but I can't guarantee any-thing."

"Okay," Peter said. He was glad that his boss was able to understand. When he finally got home, Peter called Raya's school and told them that she would not be attending school for the next week or so. After that, he woke Raya up and then they packed their bags together, ate breakfast, and headed out the door. After walking about a block, Peter called a taxi that drove them

The Giant Goldfish
JENI CRONE

to the airport. On the drive to the airport, Peter looked over at Raya who was smiling a big ol' smile and looking out the window.He hadn't seen her this happy in a long time! Then Peter realized something . . . he realized that he was excited too! All he could think about was the giant goldfish, his head flooding with questions, and he couldn't stop smiling!

When they finally got to the airport, the loudspeaker went off. "Can everybody who is on the flight from—" the loudspeaker cut off with a staticy noise. "—To Las Vegas, Nevada, please get ready to board your flight. Please have your tickets on hand . . . "

Peter looked down at Raya. "That's us!" he said. Raya looked up and nodded happily. When they got to the boarding area, there was a long line to get their tickets checked.

As they were moving up in line, Raya whispered to her father. "Are you sure you want to do this, Daddy?" she said, "I mean, I know that we don't have a lot of money . . . maybe we can wait until next year? Or maybe—"

"Raya," Peter said, "don't you worry about it. Just remember that I would do anything for you." Raya smiled and started hopping around excited. When they finally got to the front of the line, Peter and Raya were greeted by an employee who sounded like she didn't want to be there. "Tickets please," she said with an I-really-don't-wanna-be-here tone. Peter reached into his pocket, pulled out the tickets, and handed them to her.

"Sir, these tickets to Canada are not valid until next month." Peter looked confused. "Wait, where did you say that my tickets are to?" "Canada." "May I see the tickets please?" he said. And, sure enough, when Peter looked at the tickets, they were to Canada alright. "Th-There must be some kind of mistake. . . " "These tickets say Canada." "But, wait! Look here!" Peter pulled out his phone, the American Airlines website on the screen, "It says here that I purchased tickets to Las Vegas scheduled for TODAY! You guys must have given me the wrong tickets."

"Possibly," said the employee who was starting to get impatient.

"Therefore, it's not my fault that you guys gave me the wrong tickets!" said Peter. "Listen," said the employee. "There is nothing that I can do about it." "Can you at least give me a refund?" "Sorry, no refunds unless we are notified twenty-four hours before." Peter wanted to keep arguing, but it didn't look like there was anything he could do, so he leaned down to talk to Raya. "Raya," he said, "I'm so, so, so very sorry. But it doesn't look like we can't go and see the fish. Those tickets were a lot of money, and I don't think we can afford new ones . . ."

As soon as those words left his mouth, Peter could see a slight flicker of disappointment in her eyes. "I-It's okay, dad," her voice was starting to sound shaky, like she was about to cry. Raya and Peter were about to step out of the line, when Peter felt a gentle hand on his shoulder. He turned to see an old woman, staring up at him with such gentle eyes. "I'll pay as much as I can for your tickets." Peter started to shake his head. "No, no, no," he said. "You don't have to. . . we can reschedule next—"

"But I insist," she said. The old woman started to walk out of the line as Peter ran to help her with her bags. As they were walking away, Peter heard two more voices. "We can help too!" It was a young couple with a child in a stroller. "So can we!" said another voice. "I can!" "I'll be glad to help." "It would be my pleasure." "We're always willing to help anyone in need . . ."

The area started flooding with voices willing to help Raya and her father afford new tickets to Las Vegas. Almost everybody left the line to help them, and those who didn't cheered them on. Everybody pooled their money together to get two tickets for Raya and Peter. When Peter and Raya got on the plane, all Raya could think about was those amazing people who helped her see the fish. That day, Raya learned how good it was to give and that all people should stick together no matter what.

When they arrived in Las Vegas and saw the fish, they were amazed. They had never seen a more magnificent creature in their lives. Raya wondered why everybody was bored by it. The fact alone that this creature existed was already enough to make her smile. Raya and her father had a great time in Vegas, all the sights and buildings, until it was finally time to go home. When Raya got home, the only thing she wanted to do was to help other people, help those in need. Help people like the ones that helped her. She knew that as long as she helped people, she had the power to change the world.

THERE IN THE CITY AT THE OCEAN
Julian D. | Grade 7

Once, there was a girl named Candy and her father named Orange. They lived in Fort Meyers, Florida. They were on a boat going fishing for a big fish that no one had ever seen and cost a fortune.

Two hours later, they caught a giant goldfish in the ocean. Orange licked the fish next to its eye. It was from South America, from the Amazon River. Orange knew this because he was A G.F.E.A.A.R.G.F.E, A Gold Fish Expert And Amazon River Gold Fish Expert. Orange licked the fish because his tastebuds needed to gather all the DNA. Orange's tastebuds gathered all of the DNA and sent it up to his brain.

People paid money to see the fish. A few days later, nobody went to see it anymore and the fish was so sad. Orange freed the fish and he was so happy. Candy also felt happy when Orange freed the fish.

A NEW ADVENTURE

Isabella M. | Grade 5

There was a girl called Star. Star had black flowy hair. She had silver cuffs and a black suit with purple boots. She was thirteen. Her planet was called Life Two. Life Two was nice, welcoming, and friendly. Star's planet was in war with planet After. After was mean, dull, and unwelcoming. One day, both of the planets exploded. Star fell off and was falling with stars to Earth. When Star was falling she grabbed a constellation and held on to a constellation called Danny.

Danny said, "Oh my, a human breathing! Wow, hey guys! It's a human." Star said, "Huh you can talk! Oh, why did you say guys?" A bunch of constellations came out, named Lucy, Koi, Vive, Ben. All the constellations said, "Are you going to the Earth or something?" "Yes," said Star. "Well, I can give you a ride," said Koi, so they brought Star to Earth. They dropped her off at a park called Magy Dally. She fell off the bridge of the park.

In the morning, Star awoke confused. She looked around and then looked up. When she got up she saw a dark cloudy sky. It was cold. She was walking away. Star was mad, sad, confused and scared. She didn't know what to do, but just kept walking. As Star was walking she bumped into a person in bright neon raincoat.

Star said, "Wow! You're blinding me. Your skin is so bright!" Star was scared. She had never seen a raincoat because it never rained on her planet. The person in neon raincoat was startled and confused. They said, "Calm down, are you insane or are you going bananas?" "Huh?" said Star. Star felt confused and uncomfortable. Star said, "Hi, I am Star. What's your name?" "Cat," said Cat. "Do you need a place to stay? You don't look like you live here."

Star just needed a friend so now it was a new adventure.

THE GIRL WITH
THE CONSTELLATIONS

Julissa A. | Grade 4

Once upon a time there was a girl who loved constellations. The girl saw beautiful shapes in the night sky. The girl saw a heart-shaped constellation, a triangle-shaped constellation, and a circle-shaped constellation. The girl gazed at the dark sky and admired the constellations. She wished she was in the sky to be a part of the constellations. If that happened, she could have been with the constellations with weeds in her hands. The girl picked up some weeds in her hands because, with the weeds as her wings, the wind would be able to fly her up to the dark sky.

The girl smelled the fresh air that the wind blew. One night, she looked at the sky and saw the constellations out the window, and then she went out of her house and got some weeds. The wind blew her up to the dark blue and black sky with weeds in both hands. When she got up to the sky, she saw everybody's gorgeous constellations. The girl saw heart constellations, triangle constellations, circle constellations, and square constellations.

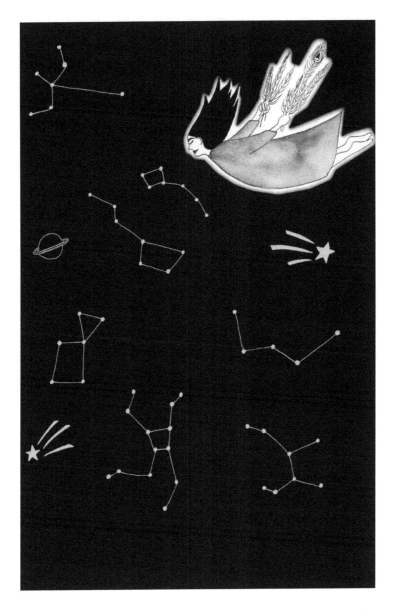

Girl In Constellations
HALLYE WEBB

THE CRANE IN THE CONSTELLATIONS

Alondra D. | Grade 8

On a small island lived a lonesome girl. An evil witch captured her and locked her up in a tower on a small island all alone because she was a princess. The witch was greedy, selfish, and mean and wanted nothing more than the princess's wealth and inheritance of the kingdom. Surprisingly, the witch was not bad looking at all. She had a great sense of style, and was very, very manipulative.

The lonesome girl wanted nothing more than to be up in the stars with the constellations, high in the sky where all her problems would just disappear. The island was completely desolate with no human activity all around and she had the view of the whole place. All she could see were the trees, animals, and the ocean. She would do anything to be up there, absolutely anything. Every day she would go up a tower with a stack of wheat and a peacock feather and pray that the constellations would allow her to join them. The wheat and peacock feather were sacrifices from her religion to her gods.

One night as she was up on the tower, she slipped off the big open window, head first to the ground. She thought for sure that would be the end for her. Little did she know every night as she prayed to be up with the constellations, they actually heard her. She had her eyes shut, ready to die, but as she fell she was slowly turning up towards space, to the stars.

Once she stopped moving, she thought to herself, *am I in heaven?* She opened her eyes and saw that all the constellations had surrounded her with warmth and happiness. She had become a crane constellation. She had always wanted to be a bright beautiful star in the sky with all the other billions of constellations. She finally felt at home and was accepted as one of their own. She would never be alone again.

ACKNOWLEDGEMENTS

We are incredibly grateful for the generosity of our donors, who fund our programs and publications. Thank you for giving our students the opportunity to become published authors and share their stories with the world. You help them creatively engage with their community, enriching the lives of their families, teachers, and peers throughout our city. Our After-School Tutoring & Writing program and this publication are both made possible in part by grants from Cartoon Network, the Charter Oak Foundation, The Margaret Baker Foundation, and the Chicago Department of Family and Support Services. Generous donations were also made by Diane Quinn, Kyle Bruck, and Kevin Boehm.

To the volunteer tutors who generously dedicate their weekday afternoons to working with this group of bright and curious young authors, we offer a colossal chorus of applause. We feel incredibly lucky to count you among the 826CHI family and are grateful for all you do.

An extra-special thanks goes out to one of our intrepid Design Cohort volunteers, Diana Molleda, who has elevated student writing with her impeccable design skills and not only laid-out this book, but also created its gorgeous cover. We are especially indebted to the care and hardwork of intern superstar Megan Cho, who lovingly gave our students editorial feedback during revisions. Thank you, Megan!

We are nothing short of astounded by the talent and commitment of our Fvall 2017 intern cohort, which includes Connie Chu, Emma Kupor, Mackenzie Lynch, Megan Cho, and Taylor Fustin. Our sincerest thanks goes to each of them for making this book possible, and for the countless other ways in which they have inspired both students and staff alike through their support of all 826CHI does.

ABOUT 826CHI

826CHI ("eight-two-six Chicago") is a nonprofit organization dedicated to supporting students ages six to eighteen with their creative and expository writing skills, and to helping teachers inspire their students to write. Our services are structured around the understanding that great leaps in learning can happen with individualized attention, and that strong writing skills are fundamental to future success.

With this in mind, we provide after-school tutoring, creative writing workshops, in-school residencies, field trips, support for English Language Learners, and publishing opportunities for Chicago youth—all at absolutely no cost to Chicago's schools, teachers, and students.

We strive for all of our programs to strengthen each student's power to express ideas effectively, creatively, confidently, and in their individual voice by providing them a safe space to be their most creative selves. Learn more at: **www.826chi.org**.

ABOUT THE WICKER PARK SECRET AGENT SUPPLY CO.

826CHI shares its space with the Wicker Park Secret Agent Supply Co., a store with a not-so-secret mission. Our unique products encourage creative writing and imaginative play, and trigger new adventures for agents of all ages.

Every purchase supports 826CHI's free programming, so visit us at 1276 N Milwaukee Ave in Wicker Park to pick up writing tools, fancy notebooks, assorted fake moustaches and other stellar disguises, books from local publishers, our latest student publications, and much more!

Or, visit us online at **www.secretagentsupply.com**.

826CHI STAFF

Kendra Curry-Khanna
Executive Director

Sankhya Amaravadi
AmeriCorps VISTA Impact & Data Coordinator

Ola Faleti
Development Coordinator

Gaby FeBland
Creative & Retail Coordinator

Waringa Hunja
Publications Manager

Melissa Kirk
AmeriCorps VISTA Volunteer Coordinator

Sarah Kokernot
Program Manager

David Pintor
Volunteer Manager

Jane Serenska
AmeriCorps VISTA Communications Coordinator

Molly Sprayregen
Program Coordinator

Tyler Stoltenberg
Operations Manager

Stien van der Ploeg
Director of Development

Maria Villarreal
Director of Programs

NOTES

NOTES

Milton Keynes UK
Ingram Content Group UK Ltd.
UKHW041825140224
437823UK00004B/149